Grade 3 Scales.
Essential Elements exercises.
Warm up flow Studies.
Jazz -

JAZZ
TRUMPET
LEVEL/GRADE 1
TUNES

THE ASSOCIATED BOARD OF THE ROYAL SCHOOLS OF MUSIC

Lead Jazz Consultant: Charles Beale
Trumpet Consultants: Chris Batchelor, Paul Jayasinha
Consultant Jazz Editors: Pete Churchill, Nikki Iles
Project Editor: Hywel Davies

Special thanks are also due to the following for their help in developing the repertoire for this project:
John Barton, Mark Bassey, Dave Bitelli, Jim Clarke, Dave Cliff, Alan Cohen, Iain Dixon, Ralf Dorrell, Digby Fairweather, Sid Gauld, Frank Griffith, Mike Hall, Stuart Hall, Eddie Harvey, Martin Hathaway, Mike Mower, Keith Nichols, Mark Nightingale, Andreas Panayi, Gerard Presencer, Brian Priestley, Simon Purcell, Geoff Simkins, Stan Sulzmann, Ray Warleigh, Huw Warren, Steve Waterman, Annie Whitehead, Tony Woods

Music setting by Barnes Music Engraving Ltd, East Sussex

designed by ● ● ● 9thplanet

Printed in England by Halstan & Co. Ltd, Amersham, Bucks.

CONTENTS

JAZZ TRUMPET
LEVEL/GRADE 1
INTRODUCTION

Welcome to this book of jazz tunes, arranged for trumpet Level/Grade 1, which forms part of the Associated Board's Jazz Syllabus. The tunes cover a wide range of styles – from gospel, blues and swing through to funk and reggae grooves – and are divided into three lists: Blues & Roots, Standards and Contemporary Jazz.

In each category there are five tunes. Each arrangement contains a fully notated HEAD, the main melody; an indication of the feel, that is straight 8s or swing; and a tempo indication (a metronome mark) representing the **minimum** exam speed for the tune at this Level/Grade. Every tune has at least one section for improvisation, marked SOLOS, with a simple chord sequence and set of guideline pitches. These pitches – appearing in boxes and shown as black noteheads without tails – give a suggested starting point to help you begin soloing. As you become more familiar with the material, you should experiment with using other pitches.

Blues & Roots draws from all periods of jazz and contains tunes based on the 12-bar blues or blues of other lengths. The list also includes African-American spirituals, other musics of New Orleans, and roots tunes from other continents. The tunes and chord sequences (or 'changes') in this list are mostly groove-based and are relatively straightforward.

Standards, as the term suggests, contains core repertoire of the jazz tradition. This includes familiar Tin Pan Alley and Broadway tunes, arranged in the rhythmic and harmonic styles of jazz, and more recent standards from swing, bebop, hard bop and other established styles. Some arrangements reproduce important past performances, while others give new perspectives on familiar tunes. Occasionally, lesser-known tunes by important performers or composers are also included. In this list, chord sequences and structures often incorporate AABA forms and II-V-I progressions.

Contemporary Jazz represents the vibrancy, eclecticism and even the fragmentation of jazz since the early 1970s. There are fusion pieces and overlaps with related styles, including rock and folk musics from around the world, plus contemporary tunes from South Africa, Europe and the American continent. Some tunes from this list were specially commissioned by the Associated Board.

JAZZ TRUMPET
LEVEL/GRADE 1
INTRODUCTION

Jazz is an aural tradition; the best way to learn is to listen to live or recorded performances. It is always good to hear how other performers have interpreted tunes you are working on, or to listen to tunes that are similar in style. With this in mind, each arrangement carries at least one Related Listening suggestion: a track, its album and record label. The availability of the listed albums has been checked as thoroughly as possible, but jazz recordings continually go in and out of issue. If you have difficulty finding them, try your local library (which usually has access to other libraries), the Internet or a specialist jazz-record supplier. In place of a specific label, 'various' indicates that the artist recorded this tune on a number of albums (including compilations) and that any of these recordings is considered suitable.

Additionally, for each arrangement, there is a footnote on the tune's history or style, its composer(s) or key performers, and, where relevant, technical advice from a jazz trumpeter. We hope that these insights provide fresh ideas and will help you develop a sense of style.

The CD at the back of this book contains a recording of each arrangement and a 'minus-one' version of the track for you to play along with. The minus-one tracks can be used in Associated Board jazz exams (we accept, however, that live accompaniment – whether small band or piano, guitar etc. – is truer to the spirit of jazz). The recorded arrangement reflects the exam routine; please note the number of bars required for the exam solo. Outside the exam – while practising or in non-exam performances – you can extend solos by repeating all or part of the SOLOS section.

At Levels/Grades 1–3 some of the tunes are arranged in keys other than the original, so that they are playable by less experienced musicians. By Level/Grade 4, however, all tunes are in their most regularly performed keys.

Jazz exams offer a great way to measure your progress, to give your work an added focus and to enable you to achieve your potential. The graded exams of the Associated Board are based on what an average student achieves during the course of one year, so that Level/Grade 5, for example, represents five years' work. At every level, candidates for these exams are assessed by musicians with broad jazz experience. For more information, please read 'Playing the Tunes in an Exam' at the back of this book.

We hope you enjoy playing these tunes as much as we have enjoyed selecting, arranging and recording them.

BLUES ORIENTAL

MILT JACKSON
arr. Iain Dixon

IT'S ME, O LORD

TRADITIONAL arr. Pete Saberton

8/6/04

Like a blues, this traditional gospel song is simple, personal and full of expression – 'It's me, it's me, it's me, O Lord, standing in the need of prayer'. Bassist Charlie Haden worked with Ornette Coleman in the 1950s and 60s, playing what became known as 'free jazz'. On *Steal Away* he and pianist Hank Jones play in a more traditional style.
RELATED LISTENING Charlie Haden and Hank Jones: 'It's me, O Lord' from *Steal Away* (Verve)

CORNERSTONE

DON DRUMMOND
arr. Chris Batchelor

17/6/04

This arrangement is an example of ska, a style of Jamaican dance music from the 1960s which developed into reggae. Notice the walking bass combined with offbeat eighth-note/quaver chords (or 'skank'), and the catchy melody. In his recording, Drummond blows (improvises) over the groove, creating the 'jazz ska' of the album title.

RELATED LISTENING Don Drummond: 'Cornerstone' from *Jazz Ska Attack 1964* (Jetset)

Published by Priestman Publishing (BMI).

SHORT STOP

SHORTY ROGERS
arr. Malcolm Miles

American trumpeter and arranger Shorty Rogers (1924–94) was a leading figure of the West Coast style of the 1950s. 'Short Stop' is a riff blues: a short, punchy rhythmic figure is repeated over a blues chord-sequence.
RELATED LISTENING Shorty Rogers: 'Short Stop' from *Short Stops* (RCA Victor)
Count Basie: 'Jumpin' at the Woodside' (various)

SWINGIN' THE BLUES

COUNT BASIE & ED DURHAM
arr. Nick Tomalin

This is a typical riff blues in the Kansas City style that influenced swing, as played by Count Basie's big band of the 1930s and 40s. Have a go at inventing your own riffs to this tune.
RELATED LISTENING Count Basie: 'Swingin' the Blues' (various)

Music by Count Basie and Ed Durham   Lyrics by Ed Durham

MOONGLOW

WILL HUDSON, EDDIE DELANGE & IRVING MILLS
arr. Pete Churchill

In the A section of this arrangement, notice how new chords with each repeat of a phrase cast the melody in a changing light. For extended solos, play whole form as AABA (where A is bars 1–8 and B is bars 17–24). Alto saxophonist, trumpeter and clarinettist Benny Carter (1907–2003) started his career in the 1920s, working with Fletcher Henderson and Duke Ellington.
RELATED LISTENING Benny Carter: 'Moonglow' from *3, 4, 5: The Verve Small Group Sessions* (Verve)

'S WONDERFUL

GEORGE & IRA GERSHWIN
arr. Pete Churchill

George Gershwin (1898–1937) was a celebrated American songwriter, pianist and composer of concert music (including the famous *Rhapsody in Blue*). ''S Wonderful' is slightly unusual in that although it is in AABA form, the tune and harmony of the third A section are markedly different from the first two As. To extend the solo form, play as AABA, where A is bars 5–12 and B is bars 21–28.

RELATED LISTENING Zoot Sims: ''S Wonderful' from *Zoot Sims and the Gershwin Brothers* (Original Jazz Classics)
Jimmy Smith: ''S Wonderful' from *The Sermon* (Blue Note)

Music and lyrics by George and Ira Gershwin
© 1927 (renewed) Chappell & Co. Inc. and New World Music Co. Ltd, USA. Warner/Chappell Music Ltd, London W6 8BS.
GERSHWIN®, GEORGE GERSHWIN® and IRA GERSHWIN™ are trademarks of Gershwin Enterprises.
Reproduced by permission of International Music Publications Ltd. All Rights Reserved.

WHEN THE SAINTS GO MARCHIN' IN

**JAMES M. BLACK &
KATHERINE PURVIS**

arr. Dave Bitelli & Charles Beale

New Orleans musicians have traditionally played this gospel tune in a jazz style. A hugely popular tune, it expresses spiritual joy in an earthy way, and appears in different forms throughout the history of jazz.
RELATED LISTENING Nicholas Payton: 'When the Saints go Marching in' from *Gumbo Nouveau* (Verve)

Music by James M. Black Lyrics by Katherine Purvis

IDAHO

JESSE STONE
arr. Pete Churchill

'Idaho' became a jazz standard in the 1940s, after being recorded by Benny Goodman and Les Hite. In the hands of Count Basie, the tune is both fast and rhythmic. Notice how well the melody swings against the driving pulse of the bass line.
RELATED LISTENING The Art Tatum, Benny Carter, Louis Bellson Trio: 'Idaho' from *The Tatum Group Masterpieces*, vol. 1 (Pablo)
Benny Carter: 'Idaho' from *A Gentleman and his Music* (Concord Jazz)
Count Basie: 'Idaho' from *Ain't Misbehavin'* (Laserlight)

Music and lyrics by Jesse Stone

IS YOU IS, OR IS YOU AIN'T (MA' BABY)?

BILLY AUSTIN & LOUIS JORDAN
arr. Pete Churchill

Saxophonist Louis Jordan (1908–75) and his group Tympany Five played rhythm-and-blues, a precursor of rock-and-roll. This tune is a great favourite with singers. Listen for the catchy lick that follows the first phrase.
RELATED LISTENING Louis Jordan: 'Is you is, or Is you ain't (ma' Baby)?' (various)

Music and lyrics by Billy Austin and Louis Jordan

STEPPIN' OUT NIKKI ILES

Nikki Iles (b. 1963) is a jazz pianist, composer and arranger, noted for recordings with Stan Sulzmann, Martin Speake and others, and for her prolific work in education. The inspiration for this tune was the wonderfully relaxed rhythm-section playing on Wayne Shorter's album *Speak No Evil*. To play the crushed note in bar 5, press down the second valve and then release it as soon as the note begins. If you have a third-valve slide, use this to tune the low Ds.

RELATED LISTENING Wayne Shorter: *Speak No Evil* (Blue Note)

JEAN PIERRE

MILES DAVIS
arr. Charles Beale

18/11/04.

Straight 8s funk ♩ = 82 **Childlike but groovy**

G|Bb|C|C#|D|F|G.

Written in 1980, this is one of Miles Davis's simplest and most ear-catching tunes. It resembles a children's rhyme or song, but over a heavy funk ostinato.
RELATED LISTENING Miles Davis: 'Jean Pierre' (various)

JUNGLE BIT
ROLAND ALPHONSO
arr. Chris Batchelor

23/11/04

Straight 8s ska ♩ = 120 **Gutsy**

The contemporary group Jazz Jamaica improvise over ska and reggae grooves like the one in this arrangement. For extended solos, use the form AAAABBAA, where A is bars 5–8 and B is bars 9–12.
RELATED LISTENING Roland Alphonso: 'Jungle Bit' from *King Size Ska* (Trojan)
Jazz Jamaica: *Skaravan* (Hannibal)

SONG, TREAD LIGHTLY

JAN GARBAREK
arr. Mike Hall

2/12/04.

Norwegian saxophonist Jan Garbarek (b. 1947) is one of the originators of the 'ECM sound', so-named after the recording label ECM. His crossover work has included playing jazz with musicians from Pakistan and with the Hilliard Ensemble, a group best known for their recordings of medieval and Renaissance music. Garbarek's own sound is beautiful and quite unmistakable.
RELATED LISTENING Jan Garbarek: 'Song, Tread Lightly' from *Rites* (ECM)

IAIN DIXON
arr. Charles Beale

This straight-8s tune cleverly uses just two phrases for the whole melody. The arrangement features gospel harmony and blues inflections. If you have a third-valve slide, use this to tune the Ds.
RELATED LISTENING Keith Jarrett: 'Country' from *My Song* (ECM), *Works* (ECM)

PLAYING THE TUNES IN AN EXAM

In the exam you are required to perform three tunes from this book, one from each list. You will also have to do a number of supporting tests, which measure your technical proficiency, musicianship and ability to improvise. For full details of the exam, please refer to the Jazz Syllabus, which is available free of charge from music retailers, our website (www.abrsm.org) or from The Associated Board of the Royal Schools of Music, 24 Portland Place, London W1B 1LU, United Kingdom.

PREPARING THE TUNES

Jazz is an aural tradition, and we expect that you will learn the tunes from the CD as well as from the printed music. For the exam, the tunes do not have to be played exactly as written, and in fact embellishment of the HEAD (as distinct from improvisation in the SOLOS section) is expected, particularly after the SOLOS section.

In the exam the following elements of the given material must be in place:

- *the correct feel* – 'straight 8s' or 'swing', as and where marked.

- *the minimum speed.* The tempo marking, representing the minimum speed, should be observed in order to demonstrate the technical control required at the Level/Grade. You may prefer to play the tune faster and this is equally acceptable.

- *the melody of the HEAD.* This may be embellished – indeed, examiners will expect some embellishment on the return of the HEAD – but it must be recognizable. Your interpretation should demonstrate an understanding of the HEAD's main musical elements, such as important kicks, other rhythmic figures and the melody's contours, and of the musical character of the arrangement.

- *the routine*, that is the form of the arrangement, with the intro (where applicable), HEAD and SOLOS containing the correct number of bars. The length of solo for the exam is indicated at the end of SOLOS, in both score and part. (Many tunes contain repeat signs around the SOLOS section, to enable you to play longer solos in non-exam performances.)

- *the improvisation.* In Level/Grade 1–3 exams the rhythmic and melodic aspects of your improvisation (in the SOLOS section) are assessed. At these early stages we expect your understanding of the relationship between melody and harmony to be developing gradually, as part of your playing, but this will not be assessed in the exam. Taking some account of the harmonic context in your solo will be given credit at Level/Grade 4 Distinction and above.

EMBELLISHING AND IMPROVISING

The process of interpreting and personalizing the tune begins once the given material is secure.

Playing the HEAD

On the first playing, the notation of the HEAD should be closely followed. While there may be variation in details of melody, rhythm or phrasing, the result should be coherent, stylish and musical, and not alter the technical level. The amount and nature of embellishment will vary from tune to tune, depending on its style and musical character.

Occasionally the HEAD contains melody notes printed in small type, accompanied by the abbreviation 'opt.' (optional). This means either that there are two commonly known versions of the tune or that it has been necessary to alter the melody slightly to suit the Level/Grade. Playing these optional notes is not a requirement of the exam, nor will they be assessed as if part of the written HEAD. However, if you prefer to include these small-type notes in the exam, you may, particularly where they form part of an embellishment.

Soloing and using guideline pitches

The guideline pitches provide a starting point for your solo. They reflect the number and range of pitches an examiner might expect to hear, and they take account of the scale requirements of the Level/Grade.

Please note that while you may use the pitches as a foundation for your solo, you will not be assessed in the exam on whether or not the guideline pitches are actually used. You will be expected to expand upon the given material as your experience allows. As your playing develops, the chords will increasingly influence the pitches you choose.

Preparing to improvise

Aim at improvising your solos and embellishing the given material at the moment of performance. Pre-prepared solos often lack the freshness, spontaneity and spirit of risk-taking that are at the heart of jazz. However, you are strongly advised to get to know the chord sequences and grooves of the tunes you have selected, and to learn as many ways through them as possible. You will then be able to demonstrate your skills in the exam through varying the musical material.

After the solo

The SOLOS section is usually followed by 'HEAD continues': the section in which the opening melody returns. Everything here may be embellished in any number of ways, from a few simple additions or variations to a more extensive reworking. As a guide, embellishment at Level/Grade 1 can mean small changes to the rhythm or melody, or variation in dynamics and phrasing. At Level/Grade 3, players might transpose material at the octave, or introduce fills. Finally, by Level/Grade 5, melodic lines may be developed with greater intricacy, and rhythms and phrasing reinterpreted. In short, exact repetition of earlier material should be avoided.

The performances on the CD demonstrate this approach, providing good examples of improvisations and embellishments of the given material. However, be inventive! Remember that examiners will be familiar with the CD and will notice slavish copying.

ACCOMPANIMENT

All the tunes must be played with an accompaniment. The options are:

- *minus-one backing-tracks*. The CD with this book includes a rhythm-section backing-track for each tune. In the exam these tracks are to be played on a portable CD player provided by the candidate. A tuning note is included on the CD.

- *written-out and improvised accompaniments*. Pianists may play from the fully written-out scores supplied with this book. Alternatively, the accompaniment may be improvised by a pianist, guitarist or other chordal accompanist, based on the written-out score, its chord symbols or a combination of the two.

- *small-band accompaniment*. Candidates may use a small band, provided the chord symbols and routines in this book are followed.

For further details, please refer to the Jazz Syllabus.

CD TRACK LISTING

TUNES
Performance/Minus-one

Blues & Roots

1	17	**BLUES ORIENTAL** Milt Jackson arr. Iain Dixon (*Kensington Music Ltd*)
2	18	**IT'S ME, O LORD** Traditional arr. Pete Saberton (*Trad./ABRSM*)
3	19	**CORNERSTONE** Don Drummond arr. Chris Batchelor (*Priestman Publishing*)
4	20	**SHORT STOP** Shorty Rogers arr. Malcolm Miles (*Michele Publishing Co.*)
5	21	**SWINGIN' THE BLUES** Count Basie & Ed Durham arr. Nick Tomalin (*Warner/Chappell Music Ltd*)

Standards

6	22	**MOONGLOW** Will Hudson, Eddie DeLange & Irving Mills arr. Pete Churchill (*MCPS Reversionary Rights/ Lafleur Music Ltd*)
7	23	**'S WONDERFUL** George & Ira Gershwin arr. Pete Churchill (*Warner/Chappell North America Ltd*)
8	24	**WHEN THE SAINTS GO MARCHIN' IN** James M. Black & Katherine Purvis arr. Dave Bitelli & Charles Beale (*PD/ABRSM*)
9	25	**IDAHO** Jesse Stone arr. Pete Churchill (*Famous Music Publishing Ltd*)
10	26	**IS YOU IS, OR IS YOU AIN'T (MA' BABY)?** Billy Austin & Louis Jordan arr. Pete Churchill (*Universal/MCA Music Ltd*)

Contemporary Jazz

11	27	**STEPPIN' OUT** Nikki Iles (*ABRSM*)
12	28	**JEAN PIERRE** Miles Davis arr. Charles Beale (*Sony/ATV Music Publishing (UK) Ltd*)
13	29	**JUNGLE BIT** Roland Alphonso arr. Chris Batchelor (*The Sparta Florida Music Group Ltd*)
14	30	**SONG, TREAD LIGHTLY** Jan Garbarek arr. Mike Hall (*Jan Garbarek*)
15	31	**AWA** Iain Dixon arr. Charles Beale (*Iain Dixon*)
16		**TUNING NOTE** concert B♭

AURAL TESTS

32	**Test A, No. 1**
33	**Test B, No. 1**
34	**Test C, No. 3**

QUICK STUDIES

| 35 | **No. 6** by ear |
| 36 | **No. 6** at sight |

SCALES

37	**Dorian on A, 1 octave** swing
38	**F major, to a fifth** straight 8s
39	**Minor pentatonic on A, 1 octave** swing
40	**C major arpeggio, 1 octave** straight 8s

Trumpet: Chris Batchelor, Paul Jayasinha, Martin Shaw
Keyboards: Robin Aspland, Pete Churchill, John Pierce, Huw Warren, Jim Watson, Gareth Williams
Bass: Jeremy Brown, Orlando Le Fleming, Matt Miles, Dudley Phillips, Steve Watts
Drums/Percussion: Paul Clarvis, Mark Fletcher, Nic France, Sebastiaan de Krom, Tristan Mailliot, Bosco de Oliveira
Guitar: John Parricelli
Examiners: Charles Beale, Nikki Iles **Exam 'Candidates':** Chris Batchelor, John Hayward, Nathan Hayward, Joanne Hughes
Producers: Charles Beale, Pete Churchill, Nikki Iles
Recording Engineer: Ken Blair
Assistant Recording Engineers: Jeremy Gill (Roundhouse), Gavin Goldberg (Metropolis), James Shannon (Surrey)

Recorded at The Roundhouse Studios, London, 25 March to 17 April and 24 June to 13 July 2002, Metropolis Studios Limited, London, 8 and 9 November 2002, and University of Surrey Studios, Guildford, 6 January 2003

A bmp production for ABRSM (Publishing) Ltd